Day White

Day was for many years a classical musician, a recitalist and an Opera singer. While singing in Ariadne by Richard Strauss, at Glyndebourne, Day met her soon-to-be husband who was in the audience. They married a year later.

When she retired from singing she trained as a Yoga teacher and has taught in England and in Scotland for the last 15 or 16 years. She lives in Oxfordshire and has 5 children and 14 grandchildren.

To Emma, Oliver, Polly, Candida and Rupert.

First published by
Brewin Books Ltd, 56 Alcester Road,
Studley, Warwickshire B80 7LG in 2014
www.brewinbooks.com

Text copyright © Day Whitelegge, 2014
Illustrations copyright © Juliet Percival, 2014

ISBN: 978-1-85858-529-1

A Cataloguing in Publication Record
for this title is available from the British Library.

Text layout by Karen Thorsen Hamer, Skandesign Ltd

Typeset in Futura
Printed in Great Britain by
Gomer Press Ltd.

Carnival of the Animals

in Yoga

Compiled & written by Day Whitelegge
Illustrated by Juliet Percival

BREWIN BOOKS

List of Contents

Foreword

It is very important to stretch the body before embarking on any Yoga exercises. There are many extensive and beneficial stretching routines but one of the simplest is as follows;

Lie on your back, on the floor, arms beside you, hands palms up.

As you breathe in float the arms up and over your head
until the back of the hands are on the floor
– now stretch, stretch, stretch.

As you breathe out float the arms down again.

Take resting breaths.

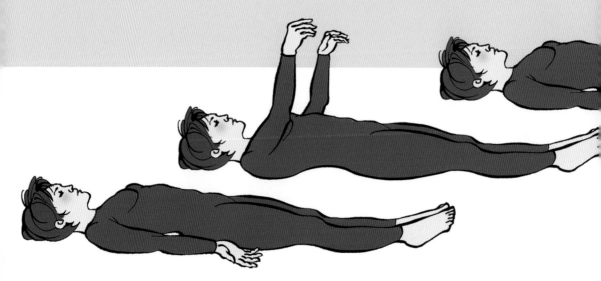

Next, keeping the legs on the floor, breathe deeply in and, turning the toes towards you, stretch, stretch the legs.

Breathe out and gently release the stretches.

Take resting breaths.

Now breathe in, float the arms up and back and stretch both legs and both arms so that the body is tense.

Hold the breath, hold the stretches.

Release the breath and gently release the stretches, floating the arms down to beside the body.

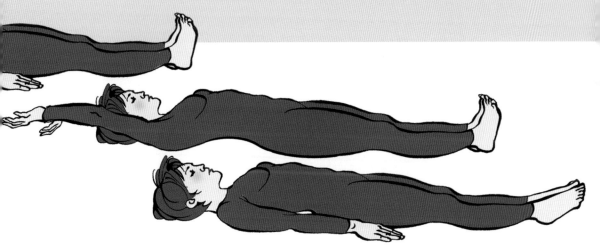

Salute to the Sun [1]

Salute to the Sun is a sequence of twelve smoothly executed moves, each one counteracting the other, expanding and contracting the chest and encouraging flexibility of the spine.

Stand erect, hands in prayer position, balls of the thumbs just below the ribs, feet together and weight evenly distributed.

Inhaling, stretch the arms up and arch the body back.

Exhaling, fold the body forward and hang, having the hands on the floor if possible.

Inhaling, bring the left leg right back, knee to the floor. Arch your back and look right up.

Salute to the Sun [2]

Until you are familiar with the sequences, don't worry too much about the breathing, very important though it is. First learn the moves and then you will find that the breathing come quite naturally and helps you to get into and out of each position.

Holding the breath bring the other leg back and have your weight on your hands and your toes. Your body should be in a straight line.

Exhaling, lower your knees, chest and forehead to the floor, toes curled under.

Inhaling, lower your hips, point your toes and hollow the back, looking up.

Exhaling, turn your toes under, soles of the feet on the floor, raise your hips and swing into the inverted position.

Salute to the Sun [3]

Inhaling, step forward with the left foot so that
it is between your hands – look up.

Exhaling, bring the feet together
and hang, having the hands palms
down on the floor if possible.

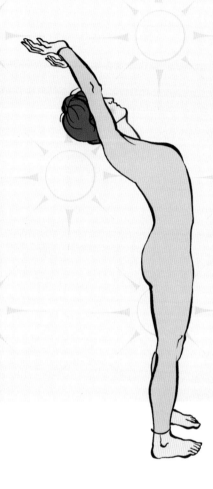

Inhaling, stretch your arms forwards
and swing up, arching the back from
the waist again.

Exhaling, come gently back
to your original position
and relax

The Lion

The Lion increases strength in the knees and thighs and relieves tension. Surprisingly, the roaring can help to soothe a sore throat. It is important to keep your knees positioned over your feet as you go down and your back straight to avoid straining either the knees or the tendons on the inside of the thighs.

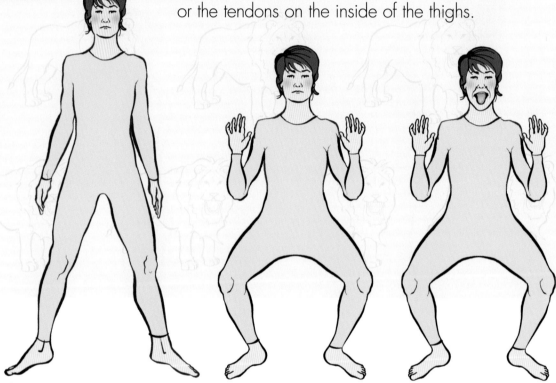

Stand with the feet a hip's width apart and a straight back. Turn the feet out. Stretch the arms up, palms to the front. Breathe in and as you breathe out bend the knees and go into a half squat.

Breathe in, straighten the knees and stretch the arms to the ceiling. Repeat. Now on the next out breath, open your mouth very wide, stick your tongue right out and roar from the back of your throat. Breathe in as you straighten up and stretch. Repeat.

Remember to keep your back straight.

The Eagle

Balances help to improve concentration and also to reduce stress because, while balancing, the mind is focussed, not on the problems or worries, but on the balance of the body.

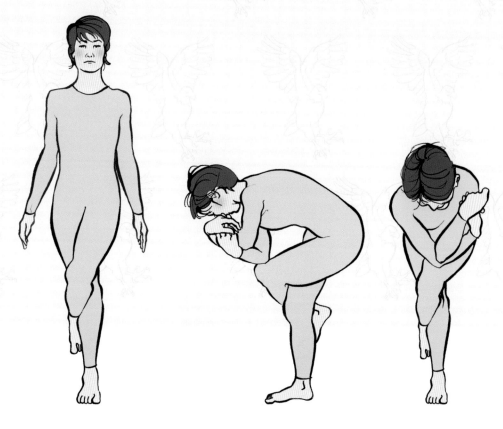

Standing, take your weight onto your right leg. Raise you left leg off the floor and twist the foot round the right shin from the front. The left foot is now behind the right shin.

Now fold your arms across your chest, bend your back and, curling up, put your right elbow on to the left knee and hold, breathing normally.

The Cobra

The Cobra benefits the abdominal regions by increasing the flow of blood. It revitalises the whole body and stimulates the thyroid.

Lie face down, hands palms down under the entire upper body.

Lift forehead, nose, chin and then the entire upper body.

Your weight will be on both hands (elbows slightly bent) your pelvis and your legs.

Look right up and don't forget to breath. Hold for 10 seconds or so increasing the time as you get familiar with the pose.

Very slowly lower your trunk to the floor and turn your head to one side.

Concentrate your mind on your lower back as you relax.

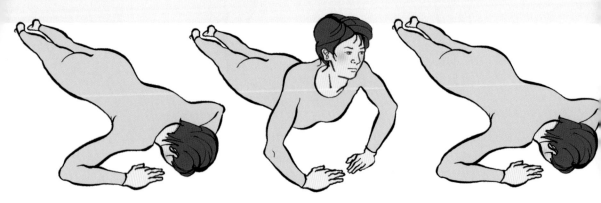

Repeat several times.

The Butterfly

The Butterfly works on the hips and knees and the tendons on the inside of the thighs. It improves flexibility.

Sit on the floor. Pull both feet towards you,
placing the soles of the feet together.
Put a hand on each knee and gently press them down,
bouncing them very lightly.

Repeat 5 - 10 times.

Straighten the legs and shake them out, then do it again.

The Cat

The Cat strengthens the back and pelvic area and revitalises the
entire body.

Breathe out and
hollow the back –
look right up.

Breathe in and
hump the back.

Kneel on all fours, hands
shoulder distance apart,
arms straight.

Now in the same
position, hump the back
(arms straight and
chin tucked in)
draw the right knee to
the face as you inhale.

Hollow the back and, as
you breathe out,
slide the right leg back
along the floor
and stretch it.

Sink down into child pose
with arms in front.

The Dog

The Dog stretch strengthens and lengthens the legs and ankles, and exercises the ham strings which tend to get shorter as we get older. It is hard on the wrists so loosen them by holding a wrist and flapping the hand about – then the other hand of course.

Kneel, having the hands under the shoulders, fingers pointing forwards and the knees about a hip width apart.

Lift the buttocks into the air and, on the outward breath, straighten the legs and ease the soles of the feet to the floor.

Gently lower the head and breathe, holding the stretch for about a minute.

Bend alternate knees raising one heel at a time,
keeping the other foot pressed firmly on the floor.

The Hare

The Hare massages the internal organs and stretches the spine. It also exercises the little bones in the neck at the top of the spine.

Kneel, sitting back on the heels. Place the forearms on the floor in front of you, fingers pointing forwards. Breathe in and, as you exhale, take the crown of the head to the floor.

When the head is firmly on the floor swing the body forward as you breathe in and swing back as you breathe out, keeping the head steady on the floor.

Come up for a rest and do the asana several times more with occasional rests.

It is important to keep the forearms to the floor except when you come up for a rest, because they act as a brake to prevent straining the neck.

Keep the forearms to the floor, except when you are resting.

The Swan

The Swan movements should be smooth as silk – you should glide as a swan glides through the water – be graceful. Your heart will slow down and your mind will become clearer and less cluttered.

As you progress with this asana you can try moving your hands further forward little by little thus increasing the elongation of your spine.

Kneel with both hands on the floor slightly turned inward.

While exhaling bend the elbows and lower the chin to the floor – inhaling move the body forward keeping the chin close to the floor.

Keeping your chin on the floor, exhale and glide back to the original position – don't sit on your heels.

You should glide as a swan glides through the water.

The Pigeon

The Pigeon lubricates the spine – in particular the lumbar area. The asana also opens the chest and strengthens the arms, wrists and shoulders.

Sit on the sitting bones on the floor with legs stretched out in front.

Tuck the left foot into the right thigh and take the right leg half way behind you. Place the hands, palms down, fingers pointing inward on the floor in front of you.

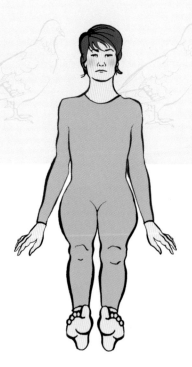

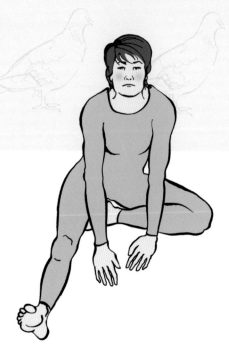

Now move the right leg further back and re-tuck the left foot into the right thigh. Repeat this, moving the hands a little until the right leg is as straight as possible behind you and the hands are over to the left. The left foot should be tucked firmly high up into the right thigh by now.

On the out breath, lower the face to the floor, bending the elbows. Breathe in and raise the head and shoulders – the hands stay in position and the elbows will still be slightly bent.

Repeat. This is your pigeon 'pecking'.

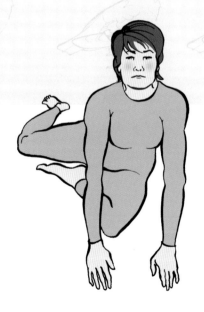

Repeat, tucking the right foot into the left thigh this time.

The Fish

The Fish exercises and compresses the cervical vertebrae and fully opens the chest. It also stimulates the thyroid and para thyroid glands.

Lie supine on the floor, feet together. Raise the trunk of the elbows, clenching the fists.

Draw the elbows back towards the head so that the crown of the head rests on the floor and the neck is stretched.

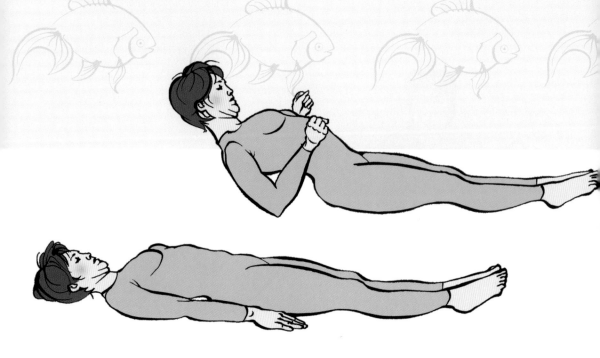

To reverse (come down) place the forearms on the floor, raise
the trunk from the waist and gently lower down.

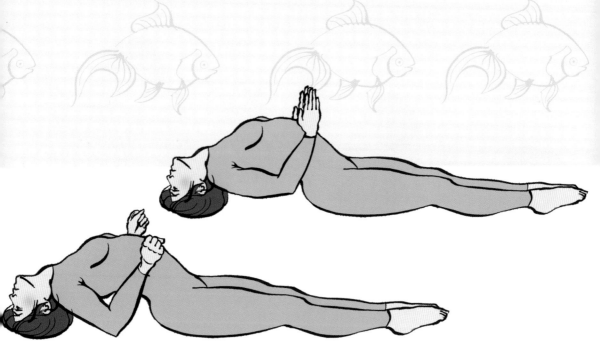

The Crane

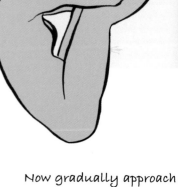

Like all balances, the Crane needs great concentration and because of this all extraneous thoughts (and worries) are banished from the mind. When you have mastered the asana and feel comfortable in it, you will sense a great feeling of achievement.

Sit on the floor with your knees bent and the soles of your feet together, hold your feet in both hands.

Now tip back until you are balanced on your coccyx (the very base of your spine) and your clasped feet, knees still bent, well off the floor.

Fixing your eyes on something static gradually straighten your legs, still holding your feet.

Now gradually approach your face to your knees, bending the elbows out to the sides.

Don't forget to breathe!

The Simple Tortoise

In this position all your soft and vulnerable parts are tucked in and protected by the 'shell' of your spine and skull. You can detach yourself from all external influences and conditions and recharge your batteries.

Curl up, bending your arms and pressing your elbows against your navel area, hands made into fists. Rest your face on your fists and hold for half a minute or so – don't forget to breathe.

Go back to Adamantine position. Repeat twice and then relax.

Kneel in the Adamantine position – hands in prayer position with the balls of the thumbs just under the ribs – back straight.

The Titiri

A small story – or perhaps a tall one?

Titiris are little birds living in India about the size of quails. It is said that they sleep on their backs with their wings spread and their claws touching their wing tips. In this position they are able to prevent the dark sky from falling onto the earth.

Lying on your back, swing your legs up into a half shoulder stand, taking the weight of your hips onto the heels of your hands.

This asana may take a little while to perfect – it is 'correct' when it is comfortable and relaxing for you. It is a version of the Pose of Tranquillity which, as its name implies, is one of the most calming positions in Yoga.

Take the legs back about half ways to the floor behind your head. Your weight will be on the back of your head and your shoulders.

Now widen the legs and put your fingers (claws) very lightly on your feet (wing tips). Breathe gently.

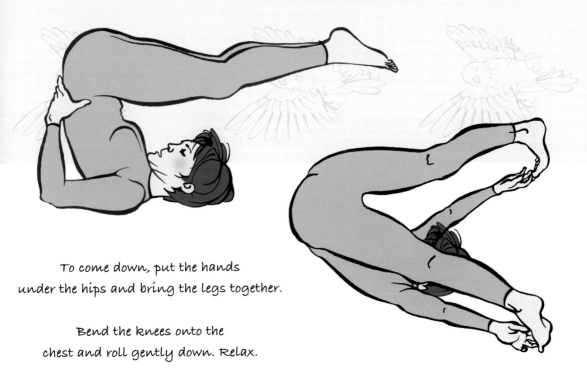

To come down, put the hands under the hips and bring the legs together.

Bend the knees onto the chest and roll gently down. Relax.

The Bird Balance

This pose may need lots of practice and perhaps a kind friend to steady you at first, but once you have mastered it you will feel a glow of achievement – not to mention a certain self satisfaction!

Kneel on all fours and put the crown of your head on the floor.

Now, keeping your forearms on the floor, curve your hands round your head.

Any balance, whether on the feet, on the head or on the side calms and concentrates the mind. The Bird Balance, being upside down, increases the flow of blood to the head and stimulates the thyroid and parathyroid.

Keeping your crown firmly on the floor, move your hands to where your elbows were.

Now lift your bottom, bend your knees up and walk your toes towards your elbows.

Lift first one knee and then the other on to your elbows, and don't forget to breathe.

The Spider

The Spider is a rather inelegant position, as shown here.

Swing your legs up until they are at right angles to the floor and take the weight of your hips onto the heels of your hands (inverted pose).

Take your legs half way back until your toes touch the floor behind your head – your arms will be flat on the floor.

(This is called the Plough which is of particular benefit to diabetics as the position has a regulating effect on the pancreas and endocrine glands.)

When you are comfortable with this position, widen your legs
and bend your knees to your ears (do breathe!).

Now fold your arms over the backs of your knees – and keep gently
breathing – yes, you can, even though you are all squashed up.

This inelegant position is called the Spider.

The Hippopotamus

The Hippo roll deeply massages the lower back helping to alleviate aches and pains in that area; it also massages and stimulates the internal organs.

Clasp your hands round your shins and, pressing your back firmly into the floor, roll the legs right over to the right.

Lying on your back, cross your ankles and draw your knees on to your chest.

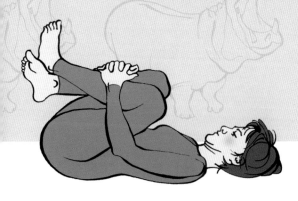

And continue the roll right over to the left. Repeat, rolling from right to left to right to left.

Push with your elbows to return to the upright position.

Salute to the Moon [1]

Salute to the Moon is a sequence of 17 smoothly executed moves.

Stand with feet a hip's width apart, arms stretch above the head, fingers pointing up.

Sway to the left and then to the right, keeping the arms close to the ears.

Bend the legs keeping the knees over the feet and roar – as in the Lion.

Salute to the Moon [2]

Arms at shoulder height with straight leg reach to the
left, then straight legged reach to the right.

Triangle to the left – look high up to your right hand.

Ankle clasp (again on the left) pull down – nose to shin.

Bend the left knee, fingers in front of your left foot . . .

Salute to the Moon [3]

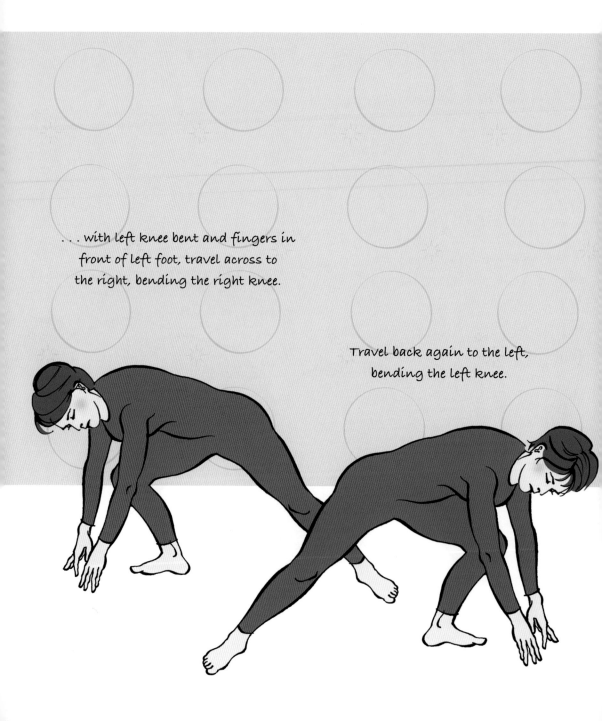

. . . with left knee bent and fingers in front of left foot, travel across to the right, bending the right knee.

Travel back again to the left, bending the left knee.

Triangle, looking high up.

Ankle clasp, pull down as before.

Salute to the Moon [4]

Straight leg to the left.

Straight leg to the right,
straight leg to the left again.

Stretch right up, bend over to the left,
over to the right. Arms up high.

Facing the front, Lion, again bending
the knees over the toes. Repeat.

References

Bikrams's Beginning Yoga Class

Complete Yoga Book – James Hewitt

Light on Yoga – B K S Lyengar

Yoga – Swami Janakananda

Healing Yoga – Swami Ambikananda Saraswati

Therapeutic Yoga – Dr Ali and Jiwan Brar

Acknowledgments

Jason Broadfield - Computer Guru, without whom . . .

Teresa Howe for her help with photography.